First Writing

This book belongs to

Educational Consultant: Betty Root

Betty Root has a lifetime of experience in education, as a teacher, lecturer and consultant.
She has written, or acted as advisor on, numerous books for primary and pre-school children.

First published in Great Britain in 1998 by Egmont UK Limited
This edition published in 2011 by Dean, an imprint of Egmont UK Limited
239 Kensington High Street, London W8 6SA

HiT entertainment

Thomas the Tank Engine & Friends™

CREATED BY BRITT ALLCROFT

Based on The Railway Series by The Reverend W Awdry
© 2011 Gullane (Thomas) LLC. A HiT Entertainment company.

Thomas the Tank Engine & Friends and Thomas & Friends are trademarks of Gullane (Thomas) Limited.
Thomas the Tank Engine & Friends and Design is Reg. U.S. Pat. & Tm. Off.

ISBN 978 0 6035 6263 1
9 10 8
Printed in Italy

Draw between the lines. Start at the dot.

Draw a line from each engine to the shed.

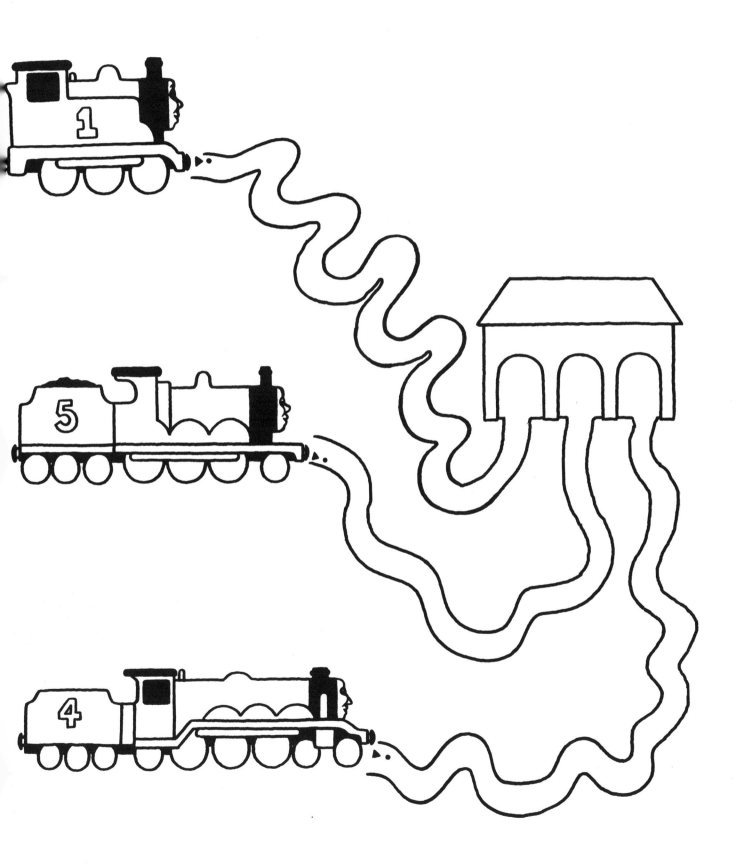

Join the dots.

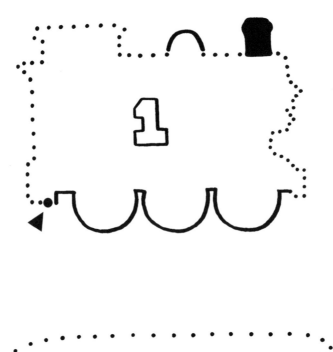

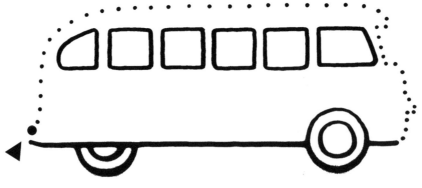

Draw over the dotted lines. Try not to touch anything with your pencil.

Which way to the station? Draw a line.

Where are Thomas and his friends going?

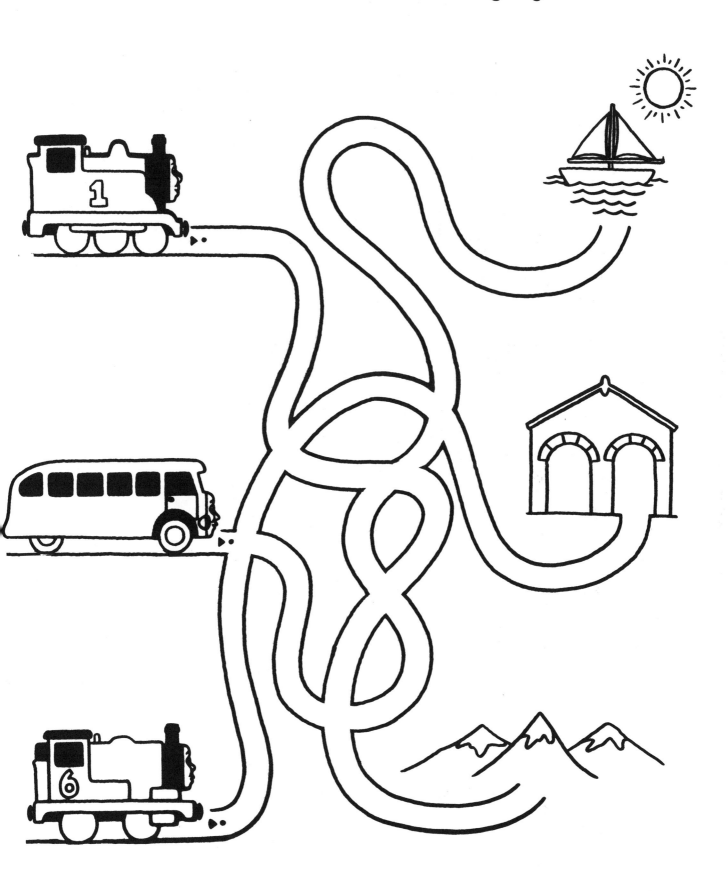

S shapes

Trace over the letter **S** with your finger. Finish the mice and balloons. Start at the dot. Draw over the other dotted lines. Then try writing some letters of your own.

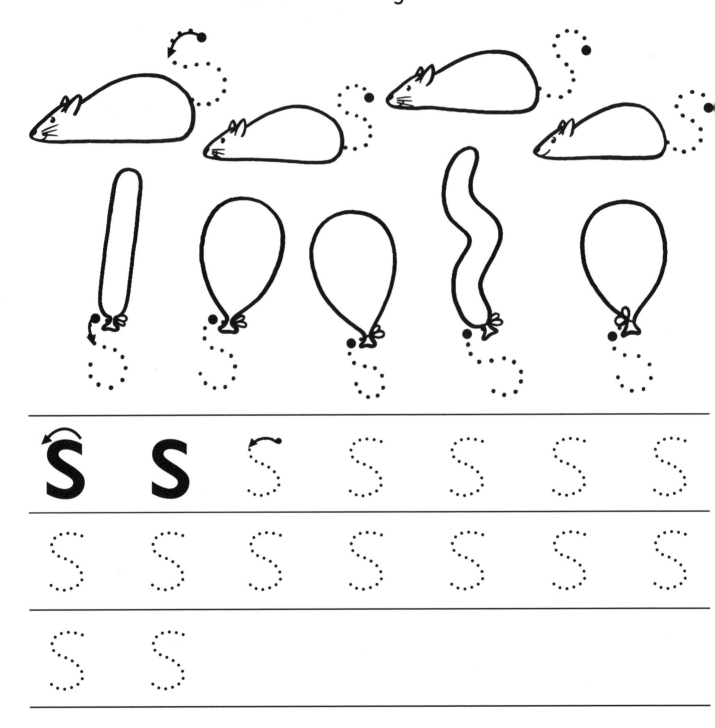

C shapes

Trace over the letter **C** with your finger. Finish the cups.
Start at the dot. Draw over the dotted lines. Then try writing
some letters of your own.

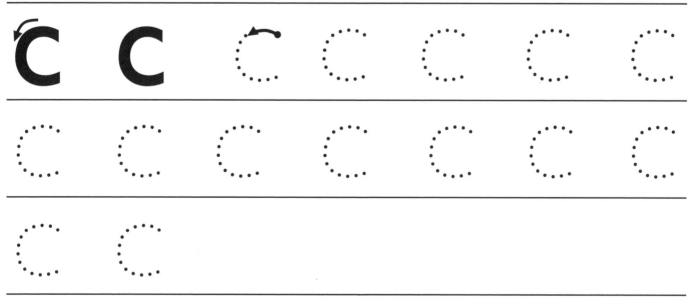

O shapes

Trace over the letter **O** with your finger. Draw wheels for Thomas and Annie. Start at the dot. Draw over the dotted lines. Then try writing some letters of your own.

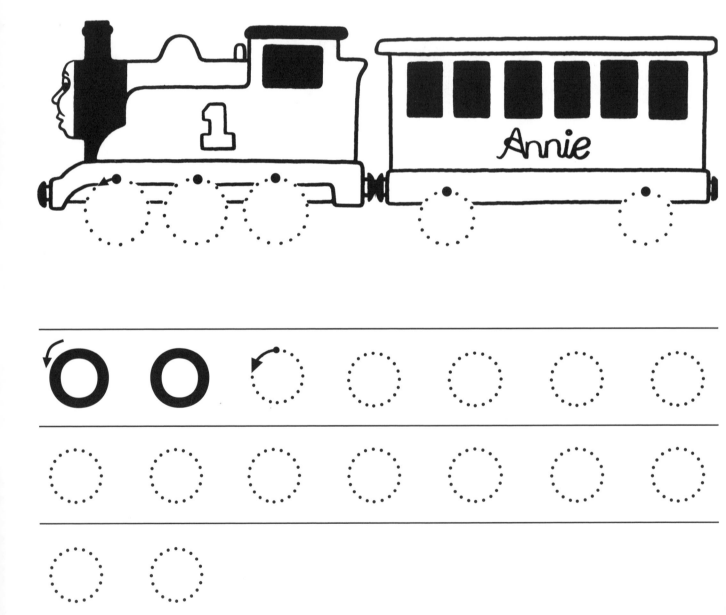

e shapes

Trace over the letter **e** with your finger. Finish the patterns in the sky. Start at the dot and draw over the dotted lines. Then try writing some letters of your own.

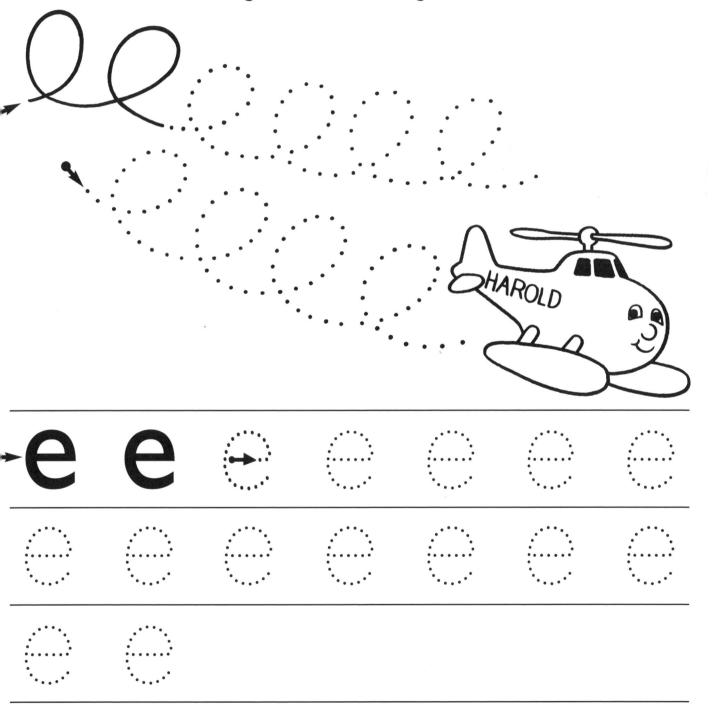

Help Thomas and his friends to find their way home.

Fill the boxes with the same letters.

Draw stems on the flowers in The Fat Controller's garden.

Follow these lines as carefully as you can.

V shapes

Trace over the letter **V** with your finger. Finish drawing the flags.
Start at the dot. Draw over the dotted lines. Then try writing
some letters of your own.

W shapes

Trace over the letter **W** with your finger. Draw over the lines to show how the balls bounce. Start at the dot. Draw over the dotted lines. Then try writing some letters of your own.

l shapes

Trace over the letter l with your finger. Draw some sticks on the flags and rungs on the ladder. Start at the dot. Draw over the dotted lines. Then try writing some letters of your own.

j shapes

Trace over the letter **j** with your finger. Draw handles on the umbrellas. Start at the dot and draw over the dotted lines. Then try writing some letters of your own.

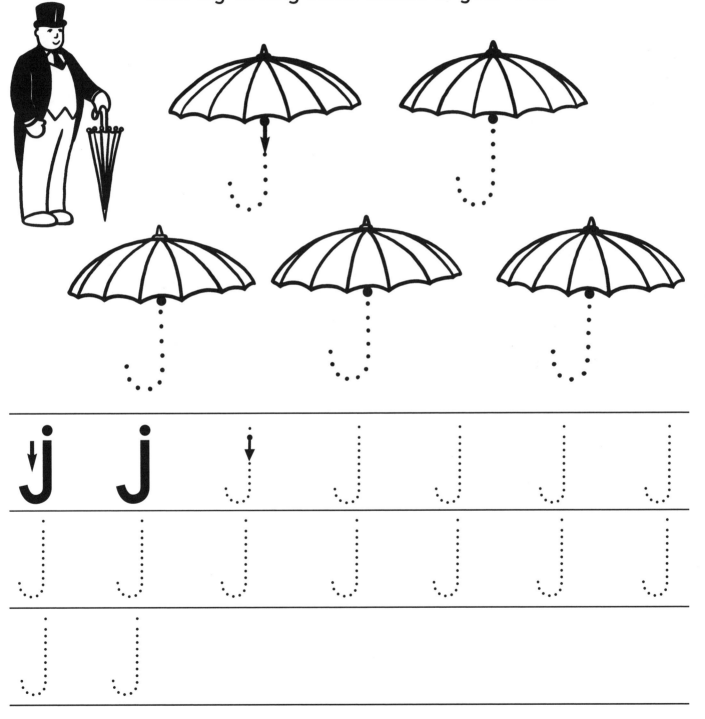

n shapes

Trace over the letter **n** with your finger. Draw some bridges and tunnels. Start at the dot. Draw over the dotted lines. Then try writing some letters of your own.

m shapes

Trace over the letter m with your finger. Finish the patterns in the field. Start at the dot. Draw over the dotted lines. Then try writing some letters of your own.

u shapes

Trace over the letter **u** with your finger. Finish the pattern on the engine shed and draw smiles on the faces. Start at the dot. Draw over the dotted lines. Then try writing some letters of your own.

u u u u u u u u u

u u u u u u u u

u u

Draw patterns on all the balloons. Now colour them in.

FIRST WRITING

This book is part of a series designed to prepare children for starting school. The following skills are covered in this book:

- holding and using a pencil in a controlled way

- forming basic letter shapes

The aim at this stage is to build confidence and make learning as much fun as possible. By working on these activities with your child, you can offer help and encouragement, and share the fun. Here are a few simple ways that you can help your child to learn.

- Start at the beginning of the book and work through each page. The activities get gradually more difficult, building on what your child has learnt.

- Short sessions are more likely to hold your child's interest, so do not try to do too much in one go. You might start with just one activity. Stop if your child is losing concentration or an activity seems too difficult: you can always come back to it later.

- Be sure to reward your child's efforts. If your child feels successful, they will be keen to learn next time.

- As children write the letters, encourage them to say the name and sound aloud. This will help them to connect the letter shape with the sound.

- An arrow shows where to begin writing each letter. It is important that your child follows this pattern and learns to form letters correctly. By writing letters the same way each time, your child will find it easier to learn the shapes and will also avoid establishing the wrong movement.

- Discuss each activity with your child to make certain that it is understood before any writing takes place. Asking questions and puzzling out the activities together is an important part of the learning process.